Allan
Ahlberg

The Night Train:
Stories in Prose and Verse

D1136831

PENGUIN BOOKS

PENGUIN BOOKS

Published by the Penguin Group
Penguin Books Ltd, 27 Wrights Lane, London W8 5TZ, England
Penguin Books USA Inc., 375 Hudson Street, New York, New York 10014, USA
Penguin Books Australia Ltd, Ringwood, Victoria, Australia
Penguin Books Canada Ltd, 10 Alcorn Avenue, Toronto, Ontario, Canada M4V 3B2
Penguin Books (NZ) Ltd, 182–190 Wairau Road, Auckland 10, New Zealand

Penguin Books Ltd, Registered Offices: Harmondsworth, Middlesex, England

**'Life Savings', 'The Night Train', 'No Man's Land', 'The Clothes Horse' and
'God Knows' first published in *The Clothes Horse and Other Stories* by Viking
Kestrel 1987 and in Puffin Books 1989; 'The Mad Professor's Daughter' first
published in *Heard it in the Playground* by Viking Kestrel 1989 and in Puffin
Books 1991; 'Captain Jim' and 'The Mighty Slide' first published in *The Mighty
Slide* by Viking Kestrel 1988 and in Puffin Books 1989**

This collection published in Penguin Books 1996
1 3 5 7 9 10 8 6 4 2

Copyright © Allan Ahlberg, 1987, 1988, 1989
All rights reserved

Set in 12.5/14.5pt Bembo Monotype
Typeset by Datix International Limited, Bungay, Suffolk
Printed in England by Clays Ltd, St Ives plc

Contents

Life Savings

THERE was once a woman who decided to save parts of her life till later, when she might have more need of them. She had the idea when she was quite young, and her parents encouraged her. The first part of her life she ever saved was half an hour from when she was four. Later, she saved a day from when she was five, another day from when she was five and a half, six days from when she was six ... and so on, all the way through her life until she was seventy.

Well, she put all these life savings in a safe in her parents' office. (They had a fortune-telling business, with a little magic on the side.) Each one had its own special box with a label giving the duration – that means how long it was – and her age.

Eventually, as I said, the woman got to be seventy and decided to spend some of her savings.

First she opened the box with a day in it from when she was eight. Her heart began to pound the moment the box was opened. She lost all interest in the office and the fortune-telling business, and rushed out into the park. Here she played on the swings and rolled on the grass and fished in the pond and ate ice-cream. By the end of the day she was worn out, but her cheeks were rosy and her eyes shone.

The next morning after breakfast the woman opened the box with a week in it from when she was ten. After that a great deal happened – and a great deal didn't happen. Dusting didn't happen, for instance, or washing-up or making an appointment at the hairdresser's. Not many bills were paid or weeds dug up. At the end of the week the woman needed another week to sort herself out. All the same her step was light as she walked about the town, and her friends said she was a changed woman.

2   Well, so it continued for some years with the

woman spending her savings bit by bit. Not all her experiences were happy, of course; life is not like that. The two days from when she was fourteen, for instance, were dreadful. She felt terribly shy *all* the time and was desperately worried about an almost invisible spot on her chin.

Then, finally, when she had used up all her life savings, the woman took to her bed, read a book for a while and – presently – died.

Some days later when friends were clearing out the office, one box of the woman's savings was discovered unopened. It was tucked away under a pile of old letters in the safe. The woman herself must not have noticed it. Its label (in her father's hand) said: Half an hour, age four.

Well, as soon as the box was opened, odd things began to happen. One of the friends went racing up and down the stairs – the office was on the third floor; another made a den under the desk, and a third played with the phone.

Of course, as you will realize, it was the last 3

half-hour of the woman's life that was causing this. Now that the woman herself was dead, it had nowhere else to go and, apparently, no reason to come to an end. In fact, as far as I know, it's still around . . . somewhere.

So, there we are. If ever you should feel the urge to act like a four-year-old (unless you *are* a four-year-old) you can blame it on the life savings of the woman in the fortune-telling business, with a little magic on the side. That's what I'd do.

The Mad Professor's Daughter

She came into the classroom
In a dress as black as night
And her eyes were green as grass
And her face was paper-white.
She was tall and quite unsmiling,
Though her manner was polite.

Yes, her manner was polite.
As she stood with Mrs Porter
And you never would have guessed
She was the Mad Professor's daughter.

'A new girl,' said the teacher.
'Her name is Margaret Bell.
She's just arrived this morning.
She's not been very well.'
And we stared into those grass-green eyes
And sank beneath their spell.

Yes, we sank beneath their spell
Like swimmers under water
And found ourselves in thrall
To the Mad Professor's daughter.

The sky outside was overcast;
Rain hung in the air
And splattered on the window panes
As we sat waiting there.
Our fate, we knew, was settled,
Yet we hardly seemed to care.

Yes, we hardly seemed to care,
As the clock ticked past the quarter,
That we had lost our lives
To the Mad Professor's daughter.

We did our sums in a sort of trance,
'Played' at half-past ten,
Sang songs in the hall for half an hour,
Ate lunch and played again.
And all the while, like a constant ache,
We wondered 'Where?' and 'When?'

Yes, where and when and how and why,
And what ill luck had brought her?
And whether we might yet deny
The Mad Professor's daughter.

She made no move at two o'clock.
She made no move at three.
A wisp of hope rose in our hearts
And thoughts of 'mum' and 'tea'.
And then she spoke the fatal words,
Just four: 'Come home with me!'

She spoke the words 'Come home with me'
The way her father taught her;
Her green eyes fixed unblinkingly,
The Mad Professor's daughter.

And now an extra sense of dread
Seeped into every soul;
The hamster cowered in its cage,
The fish flinched in its bowl.
We put our chairs up on the desks
And heard the thunder roll.

Yes, we heard the thunder roll
As we turned from Mrs Porter
And set off through the town
With the Mad Professor's daughter.

Her silent lips were red as blood.
Her step was firm (alas!)
And the people on the street
Stood aside to let us pass.
Though this piper played no tune,
She had enthralled a whole class.

A whole class, like sheep we were,
Like lambs to the slaughter,
With PE bags and such
Behind the Mad Professor's daughter.

The rain beat down upon our heads.
The wind was warm and wild.
Wet trees blew all around us,
As up a drive we filed.
Then a mad face at a window
Stared out at us – and smiled.

Yes, a mad face at a window
That streamed with running water,
While lightning lit the sky above
The Mad Professor's daughter.

And now the end has almost come;
We wait here in despair
With chains upon our arms and legs
And cobwebs in our hair.
And hear her voice outside the door,
His foot upon the stair.

Yes, his foot upon the stair:
'Oh, save us, Mrs Porter!'
Don't leave us to the father of
The Mad Professor's daughter.

A final word – a warning:
Please heed this tale I tell.
If you should meet a quiet girl
Whose name is Margaret Bell,
Don't look into her grass–green eyes
Or you'll be lost as well.

Yes, you'd be lost as well.
However hard you fought her,
And curse until the day you died
The Mad Professor's daughter.

The Night Train

SOME years ago, when the world was smaller than it is now – and a good deal flatter, come to that – the Night Train brought the night. At the end of each day, it set off with its loads of night – usually in sacks – and delivered them to the four corners of the kingdom. (I should say the world was a good deal *squarer* then, too.) It also carried large numbers of teddies and books of bedtime stories; toothbrushes, hair-rollers and tins of cocoa.

Then, at each station on the line, sacks of night were untied and the night itself rose up and enveloped the town (or village, or whatever). Of course, as you will appreciate, night came somewhat suddenly in those days. One minute you were running up to bowl, say, and the next – bang! – the moon was out. The nights could be patchy, too, and sometimes rather slow to fade away into the following morning. Well, these were disadvantages, certainly, as was the occasional sack of nightmares which the Night Train also carried. However, there were sacks of sweet dreams too, and by and large the inhabitants of the world (the King, the courtiers, the loyal subjects) all found that this arrangement with the Night Train suited them fine.

Then, suddenly, towards the end of a warm spring evening, this happened: the Night Train was held up by a gang of robbers (*dis*loyal subjects, you might call them), who robbed the passengers, kidnapped the driver, and *stole* the night.

A few hours later a ransom note was delivered to the Royal Palace. The King's secretary read it aloud to the King. 'They want a sack of gold for the driver,' she said, 'and half your kingdom for the night.'

'Half my kingdom?' cried the King. 'That's daylight robbery!'

'It's traditional, though,' his secretary said.

Meanwhile, in both halves of the kingdom there was much yawning and scratching of heads. Night-club owners were looking worried, night-school teachers were twiddling their thumbs, and the palace switchboard was jammed with calls from irate parents unable to get their children off to bed.

Well, the next day – or rather the *same* day, for the sun was still low in the sky – the King called an emergency meeting of the Royal Council together with his Chief of Police.

During the meeting, the Archbishop said, 'I believe the day of reckoning is at hand!'

The Royal Philosopher said, 'The longest day must have an end.' And (a little later), 'Tomorrow is another day!'

The Chief of Police said, 'We are searching for those robbers night and day . . . well, *day* anyway.'

And the King's Doctor said, 'An apple a day keeps the doctor away,' which was what he usually said.

After the meeting – which reached no useful conclusion – the King continued to discuss the matter with his secretary. Her advice was straightforward. 'Issue a Royal Proclamation,' she said. 'Have it proclaimed throughout the length and breadth of the land.'

'The land's square,' said the King. 'The length and breadth are the same.'

'Don't quibble,' said his secretary. 'Offer half your kingdom –'

'Not that again,' said the King.

'And the hand of your daughter in marriage, to whosoever –'

'I don't *have* a daughter,' said the King. 'I'm not even married!'

'Never mind,' said his secretary, firmly. 'It's traditional.'

Now then, whether the King would have taken this advice, I have to confess will never be known. For at this point in the story we have come to a sort of right turn, as it were. You see, 15 it is also traditional in stories involving sacks (ropes and nets, too, I believe) for *mice* to play a part. What invariably happens is, they nibble through the hero's bonds, or the net in which the lion has been captured, or – as in this case – one of the sacks of night piled up in the robbers' hideout.

Well, I've no doubt you can guess what happened next. For one thing, the hideout was not a hideout for long. Soon, hanging over it like a marker buoy, there was a small patch of dark and starry sky. (The night had poured out of the sack, you see, and escaped up the chimney.)

So then the police surrounded the place; the robbers gave themselves up; the sacks of night were loaded once more on to the Night Train, and life, in hardly any time at all, returned to normal. In the days (or rather nights) that followed, there was once more employment for night-watchmen, overtime for railway-workers and a good night's sleep for anyone who wanted it. There again, those that chose to make a night of it were free to do so; ships that wanted to pass in the night could pass in the night, and things that went *bump* in the night could . . . bump.

So there we are: what else can I tell you? Well, the robbers were sent to jail for a thousand and one nights (and days), and the King in due course married his secretary. They had grown extremely fond of each other, and besides, as the King explained when he proposed, it was traditional.

As for the Night Train, it continued to give good service for many years, until, by and by, the telescope was invented and scientists discovered the movement of the planets. The world, it turned out, wasn't square at all, but round like an orange. Furthermore, it 'rotated on its axis' (whatever that means) every twenty-four hours, causing night to follow day . . . *automatically*. (I may say, quite a few people fell *off* the earth when first they heard how fast it was spinning, and many more went about on their hands and knees for weeks.)

However, progress will not be denied, I suppose, and sure enough from that time on the Night Train was done for. Now it lies rusting and forgotten in a siding, the King's great-granddaughter rules the land and the *Gravy* Train is all the rage. Of course, it carries rather more than gravy, you understand. I mean, what use is gravy without lamb chops, for instance, and mint sauce, and roast potatoes and peas and baby carrots? And what's a dinner without a pudding: deep-dish apple pie and cinnamon and cream – and what's a pudding without . . .? But there we are, I'm getting carried away and will be into another story soon, if I don't watch it. 'The longest day must have an end', as the Royal Philosopher said, and the longest story, too, if it comes to that. So, I will stop now, desist, lay down my pen, and call it a day . . . Well, all right, a '*night*' then.

No Man's Land

THERE are all kinds of lands, as you know. There's Basutoland, where the Basutos live; Scotland, where the Scots live, and Heligoland, where the Heligos live (or maybe *go* to). There's the Land where the Bong Tree grows, and the Happy Land, far, far away. There's Cloud Cuckoo Land. There's the Land flowing with Milk and Honey (and Rice Krispies, too, I hope). And . . . there's No Man's Land.

One day a girl heard about No Man's Land and immediately began to wonder where it was and who lived there. She heard about it on the radio. Actually, she only half-heard about it. She was eating a bag of crisps at the time, and reading a comic.

Well, then the girl asked her mum and dad about No Man's Land, and they said it was the land that didn't belong to anybody – was nobody's – No *Man*'s Land.

'It could be No Woman's Land, if you like,' her mother said.

The girl, however, was not satisfied with this answer. So she went down the road to her grandma's house, and asked her.

'No Man's Land is the land where no men live,' said her grandma; 'only women and children.'

'But what about the boys?' said the girl. 'They would grow into men sooner or later.'

'All right . . . women and girls then,' said her grandma.

But the girl still wasn't satisfied. So she went further down the road to her Uncle George's house.

'No Man's Land?' said Uncle George. 'I can tell you about that. I've been there! It's the land where the *No-Men* live.'

20   'What's a "No-Man"?' said the girl.

'Something that isn't a man,' said Uncle George. Then he became all mysterious and wouldn't say any more; also the phone rang, which he had to answer.

Well, the girl was even less satisfied with this, as you can imagine. After all, *anything* isn't a man (except men . . . and boys, maybe). I mean, a *dog's* a No-Man, if you believe that – or a carrot, even – or a brick!

So, finally, the girl went right to the very end of the road where her best friend lived.

'No Man's Land? That's easy,' said her friend. She was sitting on her swing. 'It's the land where everybody says, "No".'

'Not even, "No, thank you"?' said the girl.

'No just "no",' said her friend. 'And all the men are called *No*ah, and all the women *No*la. They have loads of . . . *no*tices all over the place, and the time is always twelve o'clock – *no*on – get it?'

'And the month is always *No*vember!' said the girl.

21

'That's it – and they all speak *Nor*wegian!'

'And are as *no*sy as can be!'

'And eat nothing but . . . *noo*dles!'

At that moment the next-door neighbour came into his garden with a deckchair and a portable radio. Shortly after this, the girl heard – or half-heard, for she was eating an apple at the time – something which put all thoughts of No Man's Land right out of her head.

'Who's "*The Shadow Chancellor*"?' she said.

And her friend – in the up-rush and the down-rush of her swing – said, 'The Shadow Chancellor? . . . That's easy!'

Captain Jim

You've heard the tales of Tarzan,
Chinese Charlie Chan,
Sherlock Holmes of Baker Street
And 'cow pie' Desperate Dan;
Well, now I'm going to tell you
Of another kind of man.

Yes, now I'm going to tell you,
As the light grows dim,
And we sit here in the jungle
At the wide world's rim,
Of the man who matched them all:
And his name was Captain Jim.

Where he came from is a mystery,
Where he went to no one knows,
But his talents were amazing
(From his eyebrows to his toes!),
And his brain was full of brainwaves,
And his reputation grows.

It all began one summer
Near this very spot,
When the river-boats were steaming
And the river banks were hot,
And the *crocodiles* were teeming,
Which sometimes a child forgot.

I was playing with my brothers,
Bertie, Joe and little Frank,
In the mangrove trees that twisted
From that mossed and muddy bank;
When young Frank climbed out too far,
Slipped and fell, and straightways – sank.

Hardly had he hit the water,
Barely had the ripples spread,
When the river started foaming
And we saw with awful dread
Half a dozen snapping snouts
In a hurry to be fed.

Well, we shouted and we threw things,
Lumps of rock and bits of wood,
And young Frank, he cried for help
And tried to swim as best he could,
But the crocs were closing in
And it wasn't any good.

Then at last when all seemed lost,
And it was looking grim,
There was a *blur* beside us,
And a man leapt in to swim
Like an arrow from a bow:
And his name was Captain Jim.

He was dressed, we later noticed,
In a suit of gleaming white,
And he even had his hat on;
Oh, it was a stirring sight,
As he surged into the fray
Like a charge of dynamite.

With his bare hands and a cricket bat,
He gave the crocs what for;
Hit the six of them for six,
Though I doubt they kept the score.
Then he gave a tow to little Frank
And calmly swam to shore.

And that was the beginning,
The first time he was seen,
In the heat and haze of summer
When the air itself was green
And the river banks were steaming . . .
And he chose to intervene.

Where he came from is a mystery,
Why he stayed we never knew,
But he took a room at Macey's
And he moored his own canoe
At the wharf beside the warehouse.
And he bought a cockatoo.

Now this, I should remind you,
Was twenty years ago,
In nineteen thirty-one,
When the pace of life was slow,
And Grandpa ran the Copper Mine
And built this bungalow.

And the town was smaller then,
Just some houses and a pier,
And the Steamship Company Office
With a barber's at the rear,
And a visiting policeman
Who came by four times a year.

So it took no time at all
For the tale to get about;
How the stranger with a cricket bat
Had fished young Frankie out,
And hammered *fourteen* crocodiles
With one enormous clout.

And as the weeks went by,
There were other tales to tell:
How he saved the Baxters' baby
(With the speed of a gazelle!)
And the Baxters' baby's teddy –
It was needing help as well.

How he stopped a charging wart hog
As it rampaged through the town
(Knocking bikes and fences flying,
Pulling wires and washing down),
With a matadorial flourish
And a matadorial frown.

Well, we followed him about, of course,
Or watched him where he sat
On Macey's back verandah
In his dazzling suit and hat,
With a glass of tea beside him,
And – sometimes – Macey's cat.

We listened to the gossip
Inside the barber's shop.
Some said he was a gambler,
Some said he was a cop,
And oaths were sworn and bets were laid
On just how long he'd stop.

We eavesdropped on the talk
Outside the General Store.
They marvelled at his manicure
And at the clothes he wore.
Whoever did his laundry?
What was that cricket bat *for?*

In time the summer ended;
The rains began to fall;
Moss clung to the houses
And creepers covered all.
The river was a torrent
And the grass grew eight feet tall.

And still he lived among us
And continued to amaze,
With his quick, explosive actions,
And his steady *brainy* gaze;
Though he gave no thought to wages,
And he never looked for praise.

And he showed us how to wrestle,
And he taught us how to dive,
And he saved us from the wild bees –
We had blundered on a hive –
When he walloped it to safety
With a perfect cover drive.

He delivered Mrs Foster's fourth.
When Doc Gains fell down drunk.
(The doctor diagnosed himself:
'I'm drunker than a skunk!')
Then Captain Jim took care of *him*,
And tucked him in his bunk.

At Christmas, when a touring troupe
Arrived to do a show,
And the tenor caught a fever
And it was touch-and-go,
Who was it calmly took his place?
Well, I expect you know.

And so the seasons passed,
And the months became a year,
And he saved us from a cheetah,
And he bought us ginger beer,
And he taught us how to make our own . . .
And when to interfere.

He said: the world's a puzzle,
A game of keys and locks;
A mirror in a mirror,
A box within a box;
And we must do the best we can
And stand up to the shocks.

He told us: that's the moral,
In a world without a plan,
In a world without a meaning,
Designed to puzzle man;
You must do your intervening
In the best way that you can.

Some said he was a writer,
And some, a diplomat;
A traveller, spy, geologist,
And various things like that.
We said he was a cricketer;
How else explain the bat?

'You'd been on tour,' said little Frank.
'And scored a ton,' said Joe.
'And when the boat returned to home,'
Said I, 'you didn't go.'
But when we asked him was it true,
He said, 'Well . . . yes and no.'

And he built a bridge that summer,
And he made a mighty kite,
And he saved us from the axeman,
Who was 'axing' for a fight,
And he beat the Mayor at poker,
And he caught quail in the night.

He read the weeks-old papers,
And played the gramophone,
And climbed the hills above the town,
And watched the sky alone,
And taught the barber's daughter chess
(Who's now your Auntie Joan).

Then, one evening in September,
As we sat up on the pier,
With our mango-chutney sandwiches
And home-made ginger beer,
And our Steamboat Billy comics . . .
We saw him disappear.

In his suit of gleaming white
And his loaded-up canoe,
He passed quickly out of sight,
There was nothing we could do.
He had paid his bill at Macey's;
And he took the cockatoo.

Well, we shouted from the quayside
And we ran along the bank,
And scrambled in the mangroves,
Delayed by little Frank;
But he was gone for evermore,
And left behind . . . a blank.

Yet not quite a blank, perhaps,
For he did leave us a note
And some marbles (c/o Macey's),
And this is what he wrote:
'Watch out for life's crocodiles,
And try to stay afloat.'

Why he came remained a mystery,
Why he left us, no one knows,
But his talents were amazing
(From his eyebrows to his toes!),
And though it's now all history,
Still his reputation grows:

The voice of Nelson Eddy,
The dash of Errol Flynn,
The brains of Albert Einstein,
The speed of Rin Tin Tin,
The cover drive of Bradman,
The pluck of Gunga Din.

That's how we have remembered,
As the years grow dim
And life slips slowly by
On the wide world's rim,
The man who matched them all:
And his name was Captain Jim.

Now little Frank is bigger,
And Bertie's married Joan,
And Joe's become an engineer
With 'Wireless-Telephone',
And I tell bedtime stories
To children of my own.

One final thing, before I go
(I heard your mother call);
A few years back, it must have been,
When you were both quite small,
I bought some cigarette cards
At the Monday Market Stall.

Woodbine's Famous Cricketers,
Fifty in the set;
They were faded, creased and dog-eared,
Badly stained with dust and sweat;
Yet there was a face among them
That I never could forget.

It was him all right, I'd swear it;
It was him without a doubt,
With his bat raised in a flourish
Letting go a mighty clout.
'Captain James Fitz . . . (blur),' it stated:
'Four-forty-nine not out.'

The Clothes Horse

ONCE upon a time a magician made a horse out of clothes. He used two pairs of trousers for the legs, two pairs of shoes for the feet, a mac for the back and a tie for the tail. The head was made from a large sock, with buttons for eyes and a painted mouth. The magician cheated a little with the ears, however. They were cut out of felt and sewn on.

Well, the truth is this horse didn't look too much like a horse, when you got close to him, which I suppose was only to be expected. All the same, he had been put together by a magician, and could therefore gallop and neigh and eat his bag of oats with the best of them.

For a time the horse found himself a job pulling a milkman's cart; this was in the old days, before they had milk-floats. But he soon got bored with this and ran away (galloped away, I should say). The milkman didn't mind too much, however. He was bored with being a milkman. And the magician wasn't bothered either. He was occupied just then making a cat out of bottle tops.

Well, the horse ran away, and – to cut a long story short (or a short one shorter) – had his trousers stolen by a couple of tramps whose own trousers had worn out. His mac was taken by a little girl who wanted to make a tent with it. His tie was 'borrowed' by a man who couldn't get into a restaurant unless he was wearing one; and his sock was removed by another man (with a wooden leg) who was getting married.

Anyway, by this time there was not too much left of the horse. (There isn't too much left of the story either.) For a little while he did try walking around (or trotting, I should say) in just his shoes. But he only felt silly doing this, and besides it often scared people (dogs, too) to see four shoes coming down the road with nobody in them.

They thought it was a ghost – no, *two* ghosts!

So, finally, one bright and sunny morning the horse stepped out of his shoes and completely disappeared. Then he thought to himself: This must be the end of me! And it was.

Well, perhaps not *entirely* the end, if the truth be known. He was still *there* after all; you just couldn't see him. Anyway, what happened later (this is really another story, but I will tell it all the same), what happened later was this: The horse went back to haunt the magician and play tricks on the bottle-top cat. And after *that* he had the clever idea of stealing washing. He stole two pairs of pyjama bottoms, a couple of blankets, another sock, a sun hat . . . and so on. Finally, so I've heard, he got a job on the stage – pantomimes, mostly. Perhaps you have seen him. Of course, some people think he is really just two men dressed up as a horse. There again, you and I know better, don't we?

The Mighty Slide

The snow has fallen in the night.
The temperature's exactly right.
The playground's ready, white and wide;
Just waiting for the mighty slide.

The first to arrive is Denis Dunne.
He takes a little stuttering run.
Sideways he slides across the snow;
He moves about a yard or so,
With knees just bent and arms out wide;
And marks the beginning of the slide.

Then Martin Bannister appears,
His collar up around his ears,
His zipper zipped, his laces tied,
And follows Denis down the slide.
The snow foams up around their feet,
And melts, too, in the friction's heat.

It changes once, it changes twice:
Snow to water; water to ice.

Now others arrive: the Fisher twins
And Alice Price. A queue begins.
The slide grows longer, front and back,
Like a giant high-speed snail's track.
And flatter and greyer and glassier, too;
And as it grows, so does the queue.
Each waits in line and slides and then
Runs round and waits and slides again.

And little is said and nothing is planned,
As more and more children take a hand
(Or a foot, if you like) in the slide's construction.
They work without wages and minus
    instruction.
Like a team of cleaners to and fro
With clever feet they polish the snow.
Like a temporary tribe in wintry weather,
42 They blow on their gloves and pull together.

A dozen children, maybe more,
All skidding on the frozen floor.
The brave, like bulls, just charge the ice,
And one of these is Alice Price;
Her red scarf flying in the breeze,
You'd think she had a pair of skis.
Others approach more cautiously;
Denis for one (though he wouldn't agree).
His wobbly style is unmistakable:
The sign of a boy who knows he's breakable.

And now the slide is really growing,
And the rhythm of the queue is flowing.
Some keep a place or wait for a friend,
Some dive in the snow when they reach the end,
Some slide and pretend to be terrified,
Some stand in the queue and *never* slide.

There are children with bags and children
    without,
As they roll the silver carpet out;

And some in pairs and some in a bunch,
And one or two *eating:* an early lunch.
There's flying hair and frozen feet,
And big and little, and scruffy and neat.
There's shouting and shoving: 'Watch this!'
  'Watch me!'
'I'm floating!' 'I'm falling!' 'Oh, Mother!'
  'Wheee!'
And all the while from the frosty ground
That indescribable *sliding* sound.
Yes, snow's a pleasure and no mistake,
But the slide is the icing on the cake.

'If we knocked that wall down, moved that shed,
We could slide for miles!' the children said.
'If we knocked it *all* down – wallop – bop –
We could slide for ever and never stop!'
An icy ribbon tidily curled
In a giant circle round the world.

The slide by now is forty feet long,
And a number of things have begun to go
  wrong.
The queue stretches back to the playground
  gate;
Certain boys find it hard to wait.
While tough boys like Hoskins or Kenny Burns
Are simply not *used* to taking turns.
Like pockets of chaos or bits of sin,
They break up the queue and muscle in.

And all the time the slide gets slicker,
And the sliders slide along it quicker.
The quickest by far is Frankie Slater:
'When I grow up I'll be a skater!'
The craziest? Well, Colin Whittle;
He thinks the boy in front is a skittle.
There are bumps and bruises, bets and dares,
Cries, collisions, pile-ups, *prayers*!

But even worse than damaged kids,
The slide itself is on the skids.
The feet that brought it to perfection
Are pushing it now in a different direction.
For everything changes, that much is true;
And a part of the playground is poking through.

'It's wearing away!' 'It's wearing out!'
'We need more snow!' the children shout.
At which point Hoskins quietly swears,
And – minus the coat he never wears –
Raises his hand like a traffic cop
And calls on his fellow sliders to stop.

Then straight away from the ranks of the queue
Step Denis and Martin and Alice, too.
With no one to tell them and no one to ask,
They tackle the urgent chilly task.
They scoop the snow from either side
And bandage up the poorly slide.

Tread on it, trample it, smooth it, thump it.
'If that don't work, we'll have to jump it!'
'Jump what?' says Denis, looking queasy.
'The gap!' says Alice. 'Easy-peasy!'

Elsewhere in the playground, the usual scene:
A teacher on duty, it's Mrs Green.
A huddle of (mostly) shivering mums;
Some wondering babies, sucking thumbs
(Watching the world from way behind
As they wait in a queue of a different kind).
A gang of girls, they're shivering, too,
Discussing who'll be friends with who.
A little infant darting about,
Giving his birthday invites out.
While scattered here and there besides,
Half a dozen smaller slides.
Snowball battles, snowball chases,
Swimming kit and violin cases:
A student with a tiger skin,
And *fourteen* children to carry it in.

The slide, meanwhile, with its cold compress,
Restored to health, well, more or less,
Remains by far the star attraction,
As Denis and Co. glide back into action.
With breath like smoke and cheeks like roses,
Pounding hearts and runny noses,
Eyes a-sparkle, nerves a-quiver,
Not a chance of a chill or a sign of a shiver
(It's a funny thought, that – it's nice – it's neat:
A thing made of ice and it generates heat),
They slide and queue and slide again;
There's six in a line – no, seven – no, ten!

A motley crew, a happy band,
Attending their own strip of land.
'Fifty foot long by two foot wide!'
'By half an inch thick!' – that's the mighty slide.
Cool and grey and, now, complete.
A work of art, all done by feet.

Then, suddenly, a whistle blows,
And all the human dynamos
(With outstretched arms and just–bent knees)
Skid to a halt, fall silent, freeze.
They stand in a trance, their hot breath steaming;
Rub their eyes as though they've been
   dreaming,
Or are caught in the bossy whistle's spell,
Or simply weary – it's hard to tell.
A few of them shiver, the air feels cool;
And the thought sinks in: it's time for school.

A little while later, observe the scene,
Transformed by a whistle and Mrs Green:
The empty playground, white and wide;
The scruffy snow, the silent slide.

Inside, with a maths card just begun
And his thoughts elsewhere, sits Denis Dunne.

His hands are chapped, his socks are wet,
But in his head he's sliding yet.
He sits near a window, he stares through the
   glass.
The teacher frowns from the front of the class.
Can this boy move! Can this boy skate!
'Come on, Denis – concentrate!'
Yes, nothing changes, that much is true,
And the chances of sliding in classrooms are few.
So Denis abandons his speculation,
And gets on with his education.

Some plough the land, some mow or mine it;
While others – if you let them – shine it.

God Knows

ONCE – I will not say 'upon a time', for there was no time then, only eternity – the Children of God (there were three of them) climbed on to their Father's knee and demanded a story.

'Isn't it your Mother's turn?' said God.

'No,' said the children. 'Yours!'

So then, reluctantly, God put aside His newspaper, rubbed His chin, and began. 'Once upon a time (*He* could say that, of course; He was God) there was a place called . . . Mars.'

'We've had that already,' said the children, and they pointed through the open window to a small red planet hanging low in the night sky.

'Jupiter then,' said God.

'And that!'

'Earth?' said God.

'No,' said the children; 'not had that,' and they 51

smiled and snuggled closer together in happy expectation of what was to come.

'Well,' said God, 'once there was a place called Earth.'

As He spoke, a third planet (complete with moon) took up its position in the sky beside Jupiter and Mars – and the History of the World began.

'In the beginning,' said God, 'not a lot happened; just earthquakes – volcanoes – dust storms, that sort of thing. The atmosphere was full of ammonia and methane gas.' ('Ugh!' said the children.) 'It was pretty hot, and pretty boring. Then, after a while, the seas formed and the grass began to grow.'

Up in the sky the Earth was turning green and blue, with swirls of white cloud trailed around it, and patches of white snow at the poles.

'Did the seas have fosh in them?' said the children.

' "Fish",' said God. 'Yes, by and by. And later

there were . . . seals and frogs and turtles and alligators and antelopes and sabre-toothed tigers and . . . people.'

'No dinosaurs?' said the children. 'You had dinosaurs on Jupiter.'

'All right, dinosaurs, too,' said God. 'Only they became extinct after a time, and the people took over.'

Above them in the sky, the dinosaurs were taking leave of the Earth and preparing to become fossils. God paused for a moment and blew His nose.

'And after that things speeded up a little. There were the Pyramids and the Great Wall of China; the Battle of Hastings and the Boston Tea Party. And there was the Domesday Book and the Invention of Printing and Mozart and Charles Dickens and the Beatles.'

'What else did they invent?' said the children. 'We like the inventions.'

'Well, let's see,' said God. 'Bicycles – zip- 53

fasteners – cheese – boats and planes . . . *spaceships!* They went to the Moon.'

Now the dark side of the Earth was glittering with city lights, and a silver spaceship hung in the sky between the Earth and the Moon.

'Did they go to Mars, too?' said the children.

'By and by,' said God.

Just then a voice called from the kitchen. 'Supper's ready!'

God got to His feet with the children still in His arms. 'Good heavens!' He cried. 'Is that the time?'

After that – and when they had kissed their Mother, of course – He hurried them upstairs to bed.

On the stairs, the youngest child said, 'Do they have duncing on the Earth?'

'"Dancing",' said God. 'Oh, yes!'

And the oldest said, 'I'm going to make my own place up, one of these days. I'm going to call it . . . Pluto!'

And the middle one laughed at Pluto. 'What a name!'

God tucked them in and moved to pull the curtains across.

'Leave them open!' said the children. 'We want to look at the Earth.'

As He reached the door, the children did their best to make Him stay. 'Don't go!' they said. 'What else did they invent? What happens next?'

But God was not to be fooled. He knew what they were up to. 'What happens next?' He paused and rubbed His chin. (Meanwhile, above them in the starry sky the Earth hung, waiting.)

'God knows,' said God – and went downstairs.

PENGUIN CHILDREN'S 60s